SELF-LOVE JOURNAL FOR TEEN GIRLS

A Fun & Empowering Journal to
Build Confidence and Cultivate
Self-Awareness, Self-Love, Self-Care + Self-Growth

SELF-LOVE JOURNAL FOR TEEN GIRLS

A Fun & Empowering Journal to
Build Confidence and Cultivate
Self-Awareness, Self-Love, Self-Care + Self-Growth

TEEN THRIVE

Designed and written by Jennifer L.M. Gunn for Teen Thrive.

INSPIRATION
HERE ARE SOME BONUSES

POSTERS +

self love

LET IT GO

You Matter

*Posters are digital downloads.
Frames not included.

You Are Loved

Uniquely Beautiful

I Can do This!

10 COLORING SHEETS

DOWNLOAD USING QR CODE :

OH. HEY.

THIS JOURNAL BELONGS TO

Name

Date

THE JOURNEY BEGINS TODAY.

CONTENTS

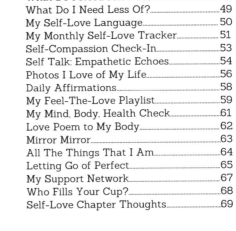

REAL TALK:

"The best love story is the one where you love yourself."

NINA LACOUR

HEY THERE!
LET'S GET STARTED.
INTRODUCTION

Hey friend! First, congratulations to you for starting this journey! Self-love can be a tricky thing, and recognizing that it's something you want to work on is a totally brave step. The thing is, self-love *really* does matter. It might sound corny, but self-love is the root of *everything*. So what the heck is self-love? Well, that's probably an important place to start.

SELF-LOVE IS THE ABILITY TO ACCEPT YOURSELF, TREAT YOURSELF WITH RESPECT, HONOR YOUR BOUNDARIES AND CARE FOR YOUR NEEDS.

That all sounds pretty straight-forward, and yet so often we do the total opposite. We're our worst critics, we don't respect ourselves, we push beyond what's comfortable and we don't always take care of our minds and bodies. Without self-love, though, we may be overly critical of our appearance or actions. We might strive for perfection and always feel like we're failing. We might find ourselves in unhealthy relationships or sabotaging our best efforts because we don't believe in our abilities. We might feel hopeless, depressed or lonely.

Self-love doesn't mean being full of yourself. It means loving yourself the way you deserve to be loved. It's an ongoing process of treating yourself with respect, setting realistic expectations, knowing and liking yourself, valuing your feelings and accepting yourself. When we don't live in a place of self-love, things can feel pretty challenging. It always feels like we're fighting a battle with ourselves. And in the end, no one wins that battle.

  ## SELF-LOVE IS A JOURNEY, NOT A DESTINATION.

HOW TO USE THIS BOOK

This book is broken down into four parts and we recommend going in order. The first part, Self-Awareness, will help you get to know yourself a bit better. In order to love yourself, you need to *really* know yourself as you are today. The second part of the book is about building Self-Love. There, you'll work on activities that help you build compassion and love for all the things that make you <u>you</u>. The third part of the book is about Self-Care, and this is where you'll focus on developing a practice of identifying and nurturing your needs. The final part of the book is about Self-Growth. Once you have developed some of the skills of self-love, you'll be ready to spread your wings. In this final section, we'll be working more deeply on building your self-love practice for long-term wellbeing.

You deserve love. Let's say that again. You deserve love. And it has to start with yourself because we can't fully accept or give love until we open our hearts. Today, you start on this path, and that is the most amazing, brilliant, incredible, inspiring, loving thing you could do.

xoxo

HOW TO USE THIS BOOK

1. GO IN ORDER >>>>>>>>>>

We recommend going in order! Each section takes you through activities and journal prompts that build upon one another. Go step by step!

2. BE HONEST WITH YOURSELF

Be honest. Don't write what you think you *should* write.
Write what you really think and feel. Growth only happens when we're honest.

3. LET EACH PART SINK IN

Don't rush through the sections. Think about them deeply.
Let them sink in a little. Take some time to reflect on each section before moving on.

4. KEEP AN OPEN MIND

Keep your mind and heart open.
You just might be surprised by what comes up or what changes within you.

5. FINISH THE WHOLE BOOK

Don't give up! Finish the whole book!
Finishing the whole journal process really will make a difference. You've got this!

3

me

SECTION 1:
SELF-AWARENESS

It's hard to love someone you don't know very well. That's why we're beginning this process of self-love by getting to know who you are today. As people, we are constantly evolving and changing — that's the really exciting thing about being human! We grow. We change. We learn.

Think about it: You're definitely not the same person you were five years ago. And five years from today, you'll have grown even more. Consider this book a time capsule, capturing the you that exists today. In learning all about her, you will open your heart to self-love.

This section focuses on who you are, what you believe, what matters most to you, big emotions, what brings you joy and exploring your wildest dreams!

Remember, there is no *should* here. Answer honestly. Don't write what you think you're "supposed" to write or what you think "sounds good." Write what you genuinely feel and think. That's the real you — and she's pretty spectacular.

Grab a pen, settle in, and let's begin.

☐ YES! I AM READY TO START MY JOURNEY OF SELF-LOVE
DATE I STARTED THIS SECTION ____/____/____

JOURNAL
Interview With Myself: Who I Am Today

My Full Name: _____

My Age: _____

I Like To: _____

I'm Good At: _____

I'm Interested In: _____

I Love to Watch: _____

My Favorite Books: _____

I Love to Eat: _____

I Like to Wear: _____

I Often Imagine: _____

I Often Wonder: _____

If I won a million dollars tomorrow, what would I do with it?

_____

_____

_____

_____

How do I spend my spare time?

_____

_____

_____

_____

I Think 💡   I Care About ♥   I Am Curious About HMMM

_____   _____   _____

_____   _____   _____

_____   _____   _____

ACTIVITY
What I Believe In

Top 5 Things I Believe In

believe

#1 _____
#2 _____
#3 _____
#4 _____
#5 _____

Top 5 Things I Stand Against

STAND UP!

#1 _____
#2 _____
#3 _____
#4 _____
#5 _____

Journal:
What's 1 opinion you have that's changed over time?
Why do you think it changed?

_____
_____
_____
_____
_____
_____
_____

ACTIVITY
My Personal Motto

life is too short to wait.

What Is a Motto?

A motto is a phrase or an expression that speaks to who you are. It's a personal slogan that represents you and what you stand for and how you live your life.

Why Should You Create One?

A motto is a quick and easy reminder of who you are. It's a memorable phrase you can use to remind yourself of what's really important in your heart.

Examples

Mottos can be quotes from others or something original.
Here are a few examples:

- "Be yourself. Everyone else is already taken."
- "We may encounter many defeats, but we must not be defeated." (Maya Angelou)
- "When they go low, we go high." (Michelle Obama)

Create Your Own Personal Motto!

Messy Ideas	The Final Choice

What Matters Most To Me

What Matters Most To Me In Life

#1 _____

#2 _____

#3 _____

#4 _____

#5 _____

The People I Love/Care About Most

#1 _____

#2 _____

#3 _____

#4 _____

#5 _____

What Possession Matters Most To Me?

_____

What Place Matters Most To Me?

_____

What Issue Matters Most to Me?

_____

Any Surprises Here?

_____

REAL TALK:

"For it's our grief that gives us our gratitude, shows us how to find hope, if we ever lose it."

AMANDA GORMAN

LET IT OUT, GIRL!

LIST YOUR HEARTBREAKS

One of the first steps toward self-love is identifying the hurts that we still carry with us. Pain comes in all shapes and sizes. Sometimes, we don't even realize how much something hurt us in life until we take the time to slow down and _really_ think about it. This can be a little hard, but it's so worth it.

THINGS THAT HURT ME　　　　　　**DO I STILL CARRY THIS WITH ME?**

_____　DEFINITELY　A LITTLE　MAYBE　NO

_____　DEFINITELY　A LITTLE　MAYBE　NO

_____　DEFINITELY　A LITTLE　MAYBE　NO

JOURNAL: HEARTBREAK DEEP DIVE

- Choose one thing from the list you made above. Now, take a _deeeeeeep_ breath.
- Put on your favorite song and let's write. Just let it out, girl!
- Explain the thing that hurt you. Let the details flow.
- Then, think about this: How do you think this heartbreak affects your life now?
- In what ways does it affect who you are?

_____

_____

_____

_____

_____

_____

_____

_____

_____

_____

_____

REFLECTION: DID IT HELP TO LET THIS OUT?　　TOTALLY!　　KINDA　　MAYBE　　NO, OUCH!

ACTIVITY
My Joys

 CELEBRATE THE GOOD!
LIST YOUR JOYS

Sometimes our heart remembers the heartbreaks a little more than the joys. The stings hit a little harder, so it's important to take the time to think about the joys in our life — no matter how small. They matter. They're everything. And by giving them attention, we can more mindfully appreciate the good in our lives. Let's dive in!

JOYS IN MY LIFE — BIG OR SMALL!   **WHAT IMPACT DOES THIS HAVE ON ME?**

_____   BIG ONE!   MEDIUM ONE.   SMALL.   NONE.

_____   BIG ONE!   MEDIUM ONE.   SMALL.   NONE.

_____   BIG ONE!   MEDIUM ONE.   SMALL.   NONE.

JOURNAL: JOY DEEP DIVE

- Choose 1 thing from the list you made above. Now, take a *deeeeeeep* breath.
- Put on your favorite song and let's write. Just let it out, girl!
- Explain the thing that brings you joy. Let the details flow.
- Then, think about this: How do you think this joy affects your life and who you are?
- Is it an ongoing thing or a one-time thing? Can you make it a bigger part of your life?
- How can you create more joy in life?

_____

_____

_____

_____

_____

_____

_____

_____

_____

_____

REFLECTION: DID IT HELP TO LET THIS OUT?   TOTALLY!   KINDA   MAYBE   NO, OUCH!

ACTIVITY
If I Could Turn Back Time

IF I COULD TURN BACK TIME

If you could turn back time, what is one thing would change?

_____

IF I COULD FIND A WAY

What would you do differently — or have happen differently?

_____

HOW DOES THIS PAST THING MAKE YOU FEEL?

_____

WHY DO YOU WANT TO CHANGE IT?

_____

_____

_____

WHAT WOULD BE DIFFERENT?

If you changed this thing from the past, what would be different now?
What long-term effect would this change have on your life or the life of others?

_____

_____

_____

⏳TAKE ACTION HOW COULD YOU MAKE THAT CHANGE <u>NOW</u>?

Time travel doesn't exist. So, is there some way you can make a difference now with this situation? Are there things you can do today to make this thing better?

_____

_____

_____

REFLECTION: HOW DID IT FEEL TO WORK THROUGH THIS?

| HELPFUL! | MADE ME THINK. | CHALLENGING. |
| WEIRD. | UNCOMFORTABLE. | UPSETTING. |

ACTIVITY
What Makes Me Unique

A Few Words To Describe Me

Something most people don't know about me is...

BE yourself

What Makes Me Special

Someone who cares about me would say I'm...

A compliment someone has given me is

Time Capsule Favorites

My Favorites

Colors	
Foods	
Smells/Scents	
Places	
Movies	
Artists/Songs	
Shows	
Books	
Restaurants	
Stores	
Hobbies	
Season	
Celebrities	
Historical Figure	
Flower	
Holiday	
Other	
Other	

ACTIVITY
Taking My Emotional Temperature

I can correctly label my own emotions when I feel them.	YES _____ NO _____ SOMETIMES _____
I recognize that emotions are temporary and change.	YES _____ NO _____ SOMETIMES _____
I recognize that emotions can affect my behavior.	YES _____ NO _____ SOMETIMES _____
I recognize that behavior can affect emotions.	YES _____ NO _____ SOMETIMES _____
I recognize that emotions can have physical effects.	YES _____ NO _____ SOMETIMES _____
I can generally manage my anger in a healthy way.	YES _____ NO _____ SOMETIMES _____
When I feel frustration or anger, I lash out, act out and/or take it out on others.	YES _____ NO _____ SOMETIMES _____
When I feel stressed, sometimes my stomach hurts or my heart races or I have trouble sleeping.	YES _____ NO _____ SOMETIMES _____
When I am afraid, I can admit it.	YES _____ NO _____ SOMETIMES _____
I am OK asking for help when I need it.	YES _____ NO _____ SOMETIMES _____
I can recognize when emotions are rising and can reach out before problems happen.	YES _____ NO _____ SOMETIMES _____

Describe a time when you were overwhelmed by emotion — positive or negative. How did you feel? How was it overwhelming? What did you do?

_____

_____

If I am struggling emotionally during the school day, what adults can I go to for help?

_____

If I am struggling emotionally late at night, where can I reach out for help?

_____

What coping mechanisms do I have for when I'm overwhelmed?

_____

LOOKING AT MY ANSWERS, I THINK I COULD USE HELP WITH:

_____ Managing Emotions

_____ Coping with Emotions

_____ Anxiety

_____ Depression

_____ Stress Management

_____ Anger Management

_____ Managing Negativity

_____ Other _____

16

ACTIVITY
The ABCS of Feelings

A
B **C**
ACTION
BELIEF
CONSEQUENCE

yes

ACTION + RATIONAL BELIEF = HEALTHY NEGATIVE EMOTION

nope

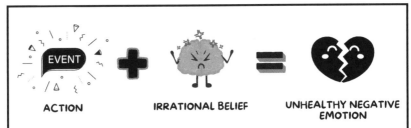

ACTION + IRRATIONAL BELIEF = UNHEALTHY NEGATIVE EMOTION

EXAMPLE

My two friends went out without me.

IRRATIONAL BELIEF
They don't like me anymore. They were probably talking behind my back the whole time.

UNHEALTHY NEGATIVE EMOTION
No one loves me. All my friends hate me. I'm not going to talk to anyone any more. I'm blocking everyone. Forget them.

My two friends went out without me.

RATIONAL BELIEF
They made plans to go see that movie. I had my Aunt's party then, so I couldn't go anyway.

HEALTHY NEGATIVE EMOTION
I'm a little bummed out that I couldn't go with them and that they went without me, but I couldn't go anyway.

NOW YOU TRY! THINK OF SOMETHING THAT MADE YOU FEEL A NEGATIVE EMOTION.

ACTION	RATIONAL BELIEF	HEALTHY NEGATIVE EMOTION
+	=	

REAL TALK:

"The beauty of a woman must be seen from in her eyes, because that is the doorway to her heart, the place where love resides."

AUDREY HEPBURN

Date This Photo Was Taken _____
Your Age _____

Paste in a selfie photo of yourself that you like.
The road to self-love begins by loving our <u>self-ie</u>.

ACTIVITY
My Emotional Reactions

Fill in the blanks to explore your emotional reactions.

FEELING WORDS

Amused	Angry	Frustrated	Secure	Determined		
Happy	Enraged	Dejected	Empowered	Anxious	Unsure	Awesome
Content	Depressed	Grateful	Inspired	Hurt	Stunned	Pessimistic
Optimistic	Desperate	Annoyed	Motivated	Stuck	Uncomfortable	Heavy
Enthusiastic	Crushed	Irritated	Refreshed	Overwhelmed	Agitated	Bitter
					Joyful	Insecure

When _I have too much school work_, I feel _overwhelmed_ and then

I give up and get super behind. .

When _____, I feel _____ and then

_____.

When _____, I feel _____ and then

_____.

When _____, I feel _____ and then

_____.

When _____, I feel _____ and then

_____.

When _____, I feel _____ and then

_____.

Choose 2 entries from above that you'd like to focus on.
Circle them or put a star * next to them.
How can being more mindful of this emotional reaction help me going forward?

_____

_____

_____

JOURNAL
What Brings Me Peace?

Turn on some music that brings you peace.
Set the mood. Do some free writing. Write about the people, places, things, smells, sights, experiences and events that bring you peace. It's important to know what brings us comfort and calm, so we can take care of ourselves when in need.

take care of your mind

ACTIVITY
My Limiting Beliefs

Limiting Beliefs are a state of mind or beliefs that hold us back. When we learn to identify them, we can better stop them from getting in the way of our success and self-love.

I would like to start an online business.

+

LIMITING BELIEFS
I'm not talented enough to do that. I don't have the money to start. I'm too young to do this.

=

CONSEQUENCES
No confidence.
No progress is made.
Giving up.
Feeling like a failure.

ACTIVATING EVENT
Something you'd like to do or accomplish.

+

LIMITING BELIEFS
Thoughts that stand in your way of accomplishing or pursuing this goal. Are these thoughts true or false? How much do you really believe these thoughts?

=

CONSEQUENCES
What have been the consequences of these limiting beliefs? How do you feel? What have you done or not done?

_____   _____   _____

_____   _____   _____

_____   _____   _____

_____   _____   _____

_____   _____   _____

FLIP IT!

Take those limiting beliefs and flip 'em!

What are some healthy, more constructive beliefs you can form to encourage yourself?

_____

_____

_____

_____

POSITIVE CONSEQUENCES

 How could these new beliefs change the game if you really started believing them?

_____

_____

_____

_____

ACTIVITY
My Confidence Boosters

Confidence is the belief that you can succeed and the willingness to take the steps toward that success. Confidence is not automatic. It's something that can be built within us. Let's take some time to identify some reasons you have to be confident. Then, you can flip back to this page any time you need a reminder.

3 Compliments That Make Me Feel Amazing

♥

♥

♥

Big or Small Ways I've Helped People

♥

♥

♥

♥

♥

reminder
Things I'm Good At

♥

♥

♥

♥

Physical Things I Like About Me

♥

♥

♥

♥

♥

3 Successes I've Had

♥

♥

♥

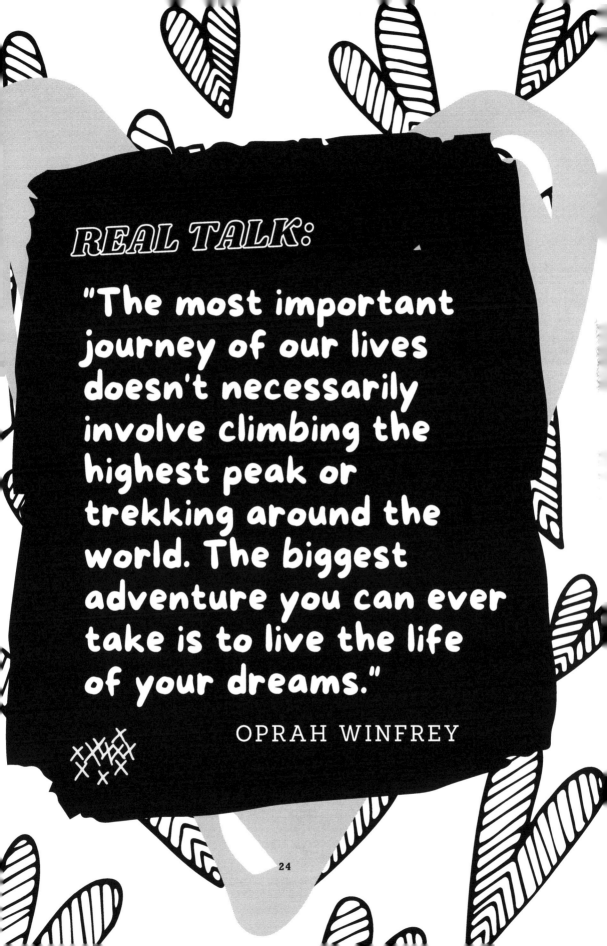

REAL TALK:

"The most important journey of our lives doesn't necessarily involve climbing the highest peak or trekking around the world. The biggest adventure you can ever take is to live the life of your dreams."

OPRAH WINFREY

No Limits - My Wildest Dreams

live your dream.

The sky is the limit. Actually, forget that. No limits, girl! In this activity, dream as big as you want! Just give yourself the freedom to think as wildly as you want. What are your biggest dreams? What dreams do you have when you're not imposing limits on yourself? What do you want in this life?

My Biggest, Wildest Dream ♥

My Other Life Dreams ♥

good things ahead

DREAM BIG

My Other Life Dreams ♥

My Other Life Dreams ♥

25

YOU CAN DO iT!

ACTIVITY
Vision Board - Visualizing My Future

"Tell me, what is it you plan to do with your one wild and precious life?"

MARY OLIVER

Vision Board

<u>WHAT TO DO:</u>
Cut out or print out images and words and tape or paste them into a collage on these 2 pages. Create a vision for who you want to be, what you want to do, where you want to go and what your life will look like.

JOURNAL
When Was I Happiest?

Turn on some music that makes you happy.
Set the mood. Do some free writing. Write about the time or times in your life when you were happiest. Tell the story. Share the details. What did you feel? What made it so great?

_____

_____

_____

_____

_____

_____

_____

_____

_____

_____

_____

_____

_____

_____

_____

_____

_____

_____

_____

_____

_____

_____

_____

_____

_____

_____

_____

_____

Let's Take a Walk

How often do you really turn off the noise in your head and take in the world around you? Tapping into sensory experiences can be incredibly calming and centering. It helps us slow down and take in the beauty around us — no matter how small. In doing this, we can learn to grow to become mindful of the little things in life and grow our love for what's around us and what's within us.

WHAT TO DO:

If you can and it's safe to do so, take a walk. Make sure you are allowed to do this and we recommend taking a buddy for safety. Don't put on any music. Allow all of your senses to take in your surroundings. Look for beauty from the smallest little flower to the clouds moving in the sky. Take notes along the way in this journal.

Where am I walking?

_____

What is the weather like?   _____

◯◯ Sights   What did I see during my walk?

_____

_____

ⅢⅢⅢⅢ Sounds   What did I hear during my walk?

_____

_____

〜〜 Smells   What did I smell during my walk?

_____

Feels
How did I feel
during my walk?   _____

ACTIVITY
Celebrating My Strengths

STAY STRONG & POWER ON

My Personal Strengths
I think my biggest strengths are

_____

_____

_____

My <u>Teachers</u> Say My Biggest Strengths Are...

_____

_____

_____

My <u>Friends/Family</u> Say My Biggest Strengths Are... (Don't Know? Ask!)

_____

_____

_____

How can these strengths help me realize my vision and dreams?

_____

_____

_____

_____

Make a List of Your Top 6 Absolute BEST Personal Qualities That Make YOU Amazing!

yeah!

YOU'RE PRETTY SPECIAL. (JUST SAYING.)

REAL TALK:

"'Thank you' is the best prayer that anyone could say. I say that one a lot. Thank you expresses extreme gratitude, humility, understanding."

ALICE WALKER

What To Do

Fill your jar by writing all of the things

you're grateful for. Gratitude is an act of self-love.

Fill your jar and fill your heart.

ACTIVITY
Would You Rather?

Get to know some of your innermost preferences with these character-based Would You Rather questions.

Would you rather be rich or be happy?
☐ ☐

Would you rather work a job you hate that pays a lot, or have your dream job with just enough money for basics?
☐ ☐

Would you rather have a large group of OK friends or a small group of really close friends?
☐ ☐

Would you rather be an expert at one thing or have common knowledge of many things?
☐ ☐

Would you rather be instantly successful or work for it and learn along the way?
☐ ☐ WORK

Would you rather fall in love once or many times?
☐ ☐

Would you rather have a best friend who is honest or who only tells you what you want to hear?
☐ FACT ☐ FAKE

Would you rather lose all your money and valuables or all the photos of your life?
☐ ☐

Would you rather be a leader or a follower?
☐ ☐

WHAT TO DO: Fill in the hearts with your passions. Feel free to color in the hearts as well!

What Sets Your Heart On Fire?

My Biggest Passion

My 2nd Biggest Passion

My 3rd Biggest Passion

Celebrate what you love!

do what makes you happy

My 4th Biggest Passion

ACTIVITY
Word on the Street

What People Say About Me

Ask 2 People
To Share 3 Positive
Things About You

Person 1 _____

✳

Person 2 _____

✳

✳

✳

Reflect: How do you feel about what was shared?
Was any of it surprising? Do you believe them? Explain your thoughts.

ACTIVITY
My Short Autobiography

Writing a short biography is a useful self-love exercise because you learn to highlight the very best of yourself while crafting a short description of who you are. Most professionals have a short bio on their résumé or web site. Let's write one now. Try writing about yourself in third person — see the example below.

EXAMPLE: Priya is an amazing writer. She is a hard worker and a loyal friend. She won the City Writing Contest last year for her poem "The Girl In the Front Row," and she regularly participates in poetry slam events in her community. She loves to help others, and volunteers at the animal shelter in her town. She loves music, ice cream and playing with her little sister. She is always learning new things and believes that she will achieve her dream of becoming a professional writer.

Write yours here!

_____

_____

_____

_____

_____

_____

_____

_____

_____

_____

_____

_____

_____

_____

_____

_____

_____

SECTION 2:
SELF-LOVE

Self-love can change your life. That's a bold statement, but it's true. When we flip the script on negative self-talk, limiting beliefs and self-doubt, we can change the course of our lives. It's that powerful. Think about your life. What could change if you had self-confidence? What could be different if you believed in yourself, instead of doubted? How could you feel if you loved yourself the way you love others? The answer is that it would be *life-altering*.

This section will help you begin your practice of self-love. It's the beginning. Self-love isn't a destination. It's an ongoing process that we engage in every day.

Be honest with yourself in this section. Open your heart to seeing who you are in new ways and letting go of old ways of thinking. Here's to breaking hurtful patterns and building bridges. You deserve this. If it feels uncomfortable, that's the stretch that tells you you're doing the hard work. You can pause whenever you need to. That's OK. Jump back in when you're ready, but don't give up.

Grab a pen. Settle in. Let's get started.

YES! I AM READY TO START THE NEXT STEP OF MY JOURNEY OF SELF-LOVE!
DATE I STARTED THIS SECTION ____/____/____

ACTIVITY
My Self-Love Roadblocks

What Stands in the Way of Loving Myself?

A LIL' PSYCHOLOGY

The Basic Needs of Human Beings

Psychologist Abraham Maslow argued that human beings have 5 basic needs that go in an order. He believed that we can't reach our full potential if these needs aren't met. So when we think about developing self-love and confidence, we have to think about the roadblocks that may exist. What needs aren't being met that could be standing in our way? Check it out.

For Example:

We can't be our best selves if we're worried about where our next meal is coming from. It's hard to love yourself and achieve your dreams if you're facing abuse or shame.

Achieving Your Potential

Self-Esteem
respect, recognition

Social/Love Needs
friendships, family, connections

Safety + Security Needs
personal safety, money, health

Physiological/Bodily Needs
food, water, rest, warmth

Maslow's Hierarchy of Needs

MY SELF-LOVE ROADBLOCKS

Look at the pyramid above. Think about and then write down what roadblocks might be standing in your way on your path to self-love.

_____

_____

_____

_____

ACTIVITY
My Self-Talk Tracker

How we frame our thinking and self-talk matters. It shapes the way we think about ourselves and ultimately how we feel. It's easy to get stuck in a cycle of negative self-talk. This week, keep track of negative self-talk messages. Then, try to change those negative messages into more constructive thoughts.

<u>Negative</u> Self Talk: I'll probably fail this test anyway.

<u>Constructive</u> Self Talk: I will do my best to prepare for this test.

Day 1

Negative Self-Talk:

Constructive Self-Talk:

Day 2

Negative Self-Talk:

Constructive Self-Talk:

Day 3

Negative Self-Talk:

Constructive Self-Talk:

Day 4

Negative Self-Talk:

Constructive Self-Talk:

Day 5

Negative Self-Talk:

Constructive Self-Talk:

ACTIVITY
Self-Talk Transformation

What is the Most Common Negative Thought You Have About Yourself?

Write it here.

What are 3 ways you can flip that thought into something constructive, positive or useful?

1

2

3

When I try hard, I can...

I am capable of...

Even when I mess up, I...

I can count on myself to...

When I doubt myself, I will try to remember...

42

ACTIVITY ♥
5 Reasons I Deserve To Be Loved

do it for you

We ALL deserve love. Especially you.
Think of **5 reasons** why <u>you</u> deserve to receive love from those in your life — and most importantly from yourself.

5 Reasons I Deserve To Be Loved

Wow. Look at that. How does that list make you feel? Why?

ACTIVITY
Reasons To Be Proud of Myself

5 Reasons To Be
Proud of Myself

Proud OF Myself

You definitely have reasons to be proud of yourself.
Maybe you overcame a big obstacle. Maybe you
accomplished something. Maybe you handled a situation
gracefully. Maybe you treated someone with kindness.
Celebrate your good by writing it down. It's helpful to see
it on paper. Be proud and give yourself some love.

Wow. Look at that. How does that list make you feel? Why?

_____

_____

_____

_____

ACTIVITY ❤
Compliments to Myself

you're doing great!

How often do you tell yourself something nice? Probably not that often. Let's do it. Look in the mirror. No, for real. Look at YOU. Think about everything you are — what you do, what you believe in, what you strive for, what you're good at. Give yourself some compliments.

Good Job!

you are enough

I am

I am

I am

I am

I am

REAL TALK:

"I've learned that fear limits you and your vision... Believing in your talents, your abilities and your self-worth can empower you to walk down an even brighter path. Transforming fear into freedom — how great is that?"

SOLEDAD O'BRIEN

ACTIVITY

Inspirational Quotes for Hard Days

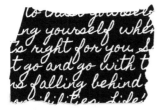

We all have tough days, but we can't let that set us back too much. Setting ourselves up to cope with hardship can make a big difference. On this page, collect some inspirational quotes from amazing people. You can come back to these quotes on hard days when you need them. Sometimes the words of others are what we need to remind ourselves that it's alllllllllllll going to be OK.

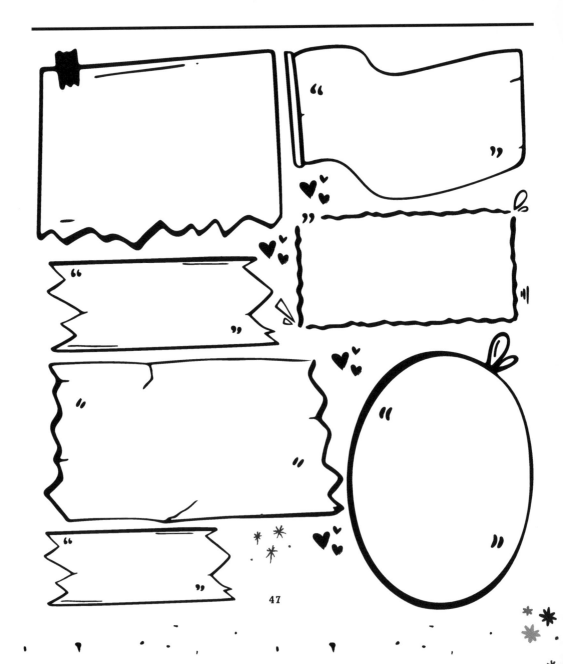

ACTIVITY
What Do I Need More of?

More, More, More...

Think about your life. What could it use more of? More free time?
More relaxation? More creativity? More fun? More laughter?
More exercise? What is missing from your life? Sit and REALLY
think about it. And make a list of 5 things.

How would having more of these five things change your life?
Can you make it happen? How?

_____

_____

_____

_____

ACTIVITY

What Do I Need Less of?

Less, Less, Less....

Think about your life. What could it use less of? Less homework? Less social media? Less drama? Less disorganization? Fewer late nights? Less worry? What do you need to shed from your life? Sit and REALLY think about it. And make a list of 5 things.

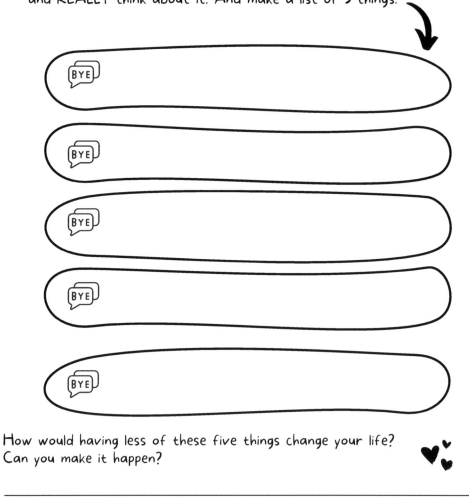

BYE

BYE

BYE

BYE

BYE

How would having less of these five things change your life? Can you make it happen?

_____

_____

_____

_____

ACTIVITY
My Self-Love Language

The 5 Love Languages

It's said that there are **5** love languages, and that everyone has different preferences for how they give and receive love. Take a look below at the **5** languages. Which language speaks most to you?

Acts of Service
Showing love by doing things for others.

Quality Time
Focused one-on-one time.

Physical Touch
Hugs and physical affection.

Words
Words of affirmation and love.

Gifts
Showing love through gift-giving.

What makes <u>you</u> feel loved?

_____
_____

How do you make others feel loved?

_____
_____

How can you better show love to yourself?

_____
_____
_____
_____

My Monthly Self-Love Action Tracker

Based on your Love Language from the previous page and the More Of/Less Of activity, let's create a monthly plan for self-love. What actions can you take to show yourself love? What habits do you want to focus on? What can you do each day and week to make yourself feel loved?

Daily Self-Love Actions

- ☐ _____
- ☐ _____
- ☐ _____
- ☐ _____
- ☐ _____
- ☐ _____
- ☐ _____

Weekly Self-Love Actions

- ☐ _____
- ☐ _____
- ☐ _____
- ☐ _____
- ☐ _____
- ☐ _____
- ☐ _____

Daily Action _____ ◊◊
○ ○ ○ ○ ○ ○ ○

Daily Action _____ ◊◊
○ ○ ○ ○ ○ ○ ○

REAL TALK:

"I've been searching for ways to heal myself, and I've found that kindness is the best way."

LADY GAGA

BE KIND

Self-Compassion Check!

When I make a mistake or fail, I get really upset and beat myself up about it.

TRUE   OR   FALSE

I frequently talk or think negatively about my appearance.

TRUE   OR   FALSE

I often doubt my ability to accomplish things and assume I'll mess things up.

TRUE   OR   FALSE

I assume most people don't like me or are thinking/talking negatively about me.

TRUE   OR   FALSE

When I am struggling emotionally, I make myself feel gulity for being weak or selfish.

TRUE   OR   FALSE

When times are hard, I try to be strict with myself so I get stronger and tougher.

TRUE   OR   FALSE

I see my flaws as intolerable and can't see past them.

TRUE   OR   FALSE

MOSTLY TRUE
If you answered true more often than false, then it looks like you might be being a little hard on yourself. Self-compassion is a form of self-love. We can work on it!

MOSTLY FALSE
If you answered false more often than true, then yay! You are compassionate and kind to yourself! Keep it up! Self-compassion is self-love!

♥ ACTIVITY
Empathetic Echoes

Answering My Self-Talk With Empathy + Love

YOU MATTER

Example

Negative Self-Talk

I hate my body.
I never look good in
anything I wear. I'm
never eating again.

Empathetic Echo

This is unkind.
I would never say
this to a friend.
Food gives us
strength and
energy. I am
beautiful. Bodies
come in all shapes
and sizes. I will be
more kind to myself.

Empathy is the ability to
understand the feelings
of others. Being
empathetic is treating
someone with compassion
by acknowledging and
respecting their feelings.

LOVE YOURSELF

Think about thoughts and things
you've said to yourself that haven't
been that kind. It can be recent or
from a long time ago.

Maybe go back to pages 41-42 and
look your Self-Talk journaling. We're
going to do a deeper dive into how you
can transform your negative self-talk
with empathetic ech
oes. On the next page, take two
examples of your negative self-talk
and transform those words into
empathetic echoes!

Negative Self-Talk

Empathetic Echo

Negative Self-Talk

Empathetic Echo

ACTIVITY
Photos I Love of My Life

Photo Collage Paste or tape in photos you love from your life.

ACTIVITY

Photos I Love of My Life

ACTIVITY
Daily Affirmations

Affirmations

Affirmations are phrases or statements that we say to ourselves to send positive messages or remind ourselves of messages we need to hear. Repeating these phrases help to train our brains to receive the love and strength we need to reach our goals or shift our thinking. Below, you'll create some affirmations to say to yourself morning, noon and night. These should be personal to your needs. Feel free to look online for inspiration!

Examples

All I need is within me right now.

I am strong and capable.

I am not my mistakes.

I believe in the woman I am becoming.

Morning

Afternoon

Night

Music That Makes Me Feel the Love

My Feel-The-Love Playlist 🎵

Let's create the ultimate self-love playlist.
Find **5** songs that make you feel empowered,
confident, loved and amazing! Then, listen on repeat!

What are your favorite song lyrics ever? Why do they speak
to you? Write about them here!

_____
_____
_____
_____
_____

REAL TALK:

"I can't think of a better representation of beauty than someone who is unafraid to be herself."

EMMA STONE

✓ SELF-CHECK

MIND

I think my mind

is healthy   needs some love   is a work in progress   is a hot mess

■■■■■■■■■■■■■■■I

BODY

I think my body

is healthy   needs some love   is a work in progress   is a hot mess

■■■■■■■■■■■■■■■I

HEALTH

I think my health

is strong   needs some attention   is in progress   is a hot mess

■■■■■■■■■■■■■■■I

SOUL

I think my soul

is healthy   needs some love   is a work in progress   is a hot mess

ACTIVITY
Ode to My Body

Write a Love Poem To Your Body

Your body is your vessel. Every body has flaws, but every body also has beauty. Your body has strength. It has a life force. Write a love poem to your body — even if you have to dig deep to do it. Read it out loud every day and help your heart and mind believe the hype — that you are, in fact, amazing!

What's an ode? A lyric poem that celebrates a person, place or thing.

Ode to My Body

ACTIVITY

Mirror, Mirror On the Wall

Look in the mirror. No, REALLY REALLY look. Examine yourself from all angles. But instead of focusing on and saying all of the things you usually say — only allow yourself to say and think kind things. Disrupt all negative self-talk. Remember those empathetic echoes? Transform your negative self-talk into empowering, loving kindness. Flaws are normal. They don't take away from your awesomeness. Focus on your fierceness. Write down some self-love noticings in the box below.

Mirror, Mirror On the Wall, I Will Be Kind To Myself After All

ACTIVITY
All The Things I Am

All The Things That I Am

On each burst, write positive, empowering, kind words that describe you. Start with the biggest bursts to write words that describe you most and work your way down to the smaller bursts. Turn and fill up the entire starburst with as many words as you can!

me

ACTIVITY
Letting Go of Perfect

Pssst! Guess what? Perfection doesn't exist. Always striving for perfection can make us feel like we're always failing. And that can reeeeeally mess with our self-love. Instead, focus on progress over perfection. We are all works in progress. Healthy striving is the key to real success and fulfillment. Be proud of yourself!

Striving VS. Perfectionism

✓  Proud OF Myself

VS

☒ WORRYING ABOUT WHAT OTHERS WILL THINK

ONE GOAL OR PROJECT IN YOUR LIFE _____

GREATNESS ♥

IT IS_____.

Striving for the possible. I can

_____

Mistakes are to be expected and they're an opportunity to learn.

What mistakes did I make in this process?

_____

How did I learn from these mistakes?

_____
_____
_____

What reasonable standards did I set?

_____

PERFECTIONISM

IT SHOULD BE _____

Striving for the impossible. I think I should

_____

Trying to be perfect, mistakes feel like failure. When we focus on perfectionism, we tend to obsess about mistakes and can't get past them.

How did mistakes slow me down when trying to be perfect?

_____
_____

What impossible standard did I set trying to be perfect? How did this hold me back?

_____
_____

REAL TALK:

"I always tell young girls, surround yourself with goodness. I learned early on how to get the haters out of my life." MICHELLE OBAMA

NAME:

- - - - - - - -

NAME:

- - - - - - - -

NAME:

- - - - - - - -

NAME:

- - - - - - - -

me

NAME:

- - - - - - - -

NAME:

- - - - - - - -

NAME:

- - - - - - - -

WHAT TO DO:
Write the name of all the people in your personal support network. Friends, family, allies, important adults, etc.

*If you don't have anyone, put the <u>types</u> of people you would like to find in your life — friends, therapists, family members, partners, allies, etc.

What's Missing?

67

ACTIVITY
Filling Up My Relationship Cup

Who Fills Your Cup?

Label each cup with someone in your life who fills your life with something good. Then, color in the cup with how much good they bring to your life.

Refilling the Cup

This cup represents a relationship in your life that needs a little work. Label the cup with a name. Then, on the drink container, write what you think the relationship needs. In the spill blob, write down what you think the relationship needs less of. Think about how and if you can repair this relationship.

Look back at the pages you've done in this section. What have you uncovered? What have you learned about yourself? What can you take with you into the next section? Don't skip out on processing all of this amazing work you've done. Let it sink in. Write about it. Think on it.

SELF-LOVE JOURNAL FOR TEEN GIRLS

SECTION 3: SELF-CARE

Self-care is about taking the time to do the things that help you live your best life. This includes everything from hygiene to caring for your mental health to setting up routines that make your life manageable *and* enjoyable. Living in survival mode and not giving yourself the gift of self-care can cause unnecessary stress and anxiety. Taking the time to care for your physical, mental and emotional health is the ultimate act of self-love.

This section will help you begin your practice of self-care. It will teach you how to build new habits, how to start a practice of positive self-talk, and how to identify your more important care needs. Self-care isn't selfish. You can care more deeply for others when you've taken care of yourself well.

Be honest with yourself in this section. Open your mind and heart and be willing to start new routines and try new ways of doing things. Ask yourself the hard questions and be brave enough to answer them with honesty. That's where the change happens. You've done so much growth already. It's exciting to see where you'll go next. Grab a pen. Settle in. Let's get started.

☐ YES! I AM READY TO START THE NEXT STEP OF MY JOURNEY OF SELF-LOVE!
DATE I STARTED THIS SECTION ____/____/____

ACTIVITY
My Stress Factors

Let's Stop Stressin'

Stress is a major deal. It actually impacts our mind, our body and our spirit. Feeling stressed out can take a toll on our health, and it impacts how we sleep, eat and even how we fight off illness. Stress can also make it harder to regulate our moods. It's important to first know the things that stress us out, so that we can be more mindful and ready to cope with them when they arise.

What Are My Stress Factors?

BIG STRESSOR

BIGGEST STRESSOR

MEDIUM STRESSOR

MEDIUM STRESSOR

SMALLEST STRESSOR

MINOR STRESSOR

What <u>consistently</u> stresses me out the most?

_____

Keep Calm & Carry On

We all need calm in our lives. Whether it's quiet time, hobbies, meditation, a pet, a favorite show, music or a beautiful place in nature, knowing the things that bring you calm gives you the tools you need to handle stressful times.

What Brings Me Calm

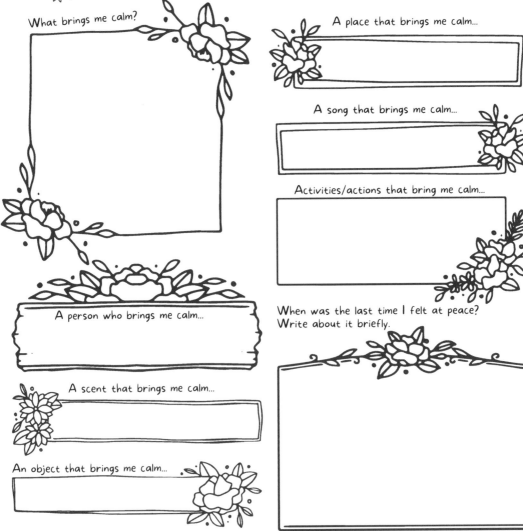

What brings me calm?

A place that brings me calm...

A song that brings me calm...

Activities/actions that bring me calm...

A person who brings me calm...

When was the last time I felt at peace? Write about it briefly.

A scent that brings me calm...

An object that brings me calm...

ACTIVITY
My Self-Care Roadblocks

What Stands in the Way of Caring For Myself?

WHAT IS SELF-CARE?

Personal

Knowing yourself.
Enjoying hobbies.
Goal-setting.
Pursuing passions.
Living by your values.
Honoring your boundaries.

Physical

Getting proper sleep/rest.
Getting regular exercise.
Prioritizing health.
Good nutrition.
Stretching.
Daily hygiene.
Meditation/reflection.

Emotional

Being kind to yourself and others.
Managing stress.
Taking care of your mental health needs.
Maintaining boundaries.

Social

Building healthy support systems.
Socializing with supportive friend groups.
Open lines of communication.

MY SELF-CARE ROADBLOCKS

Look at the lists above. Think about it and then write down what roadblocks might be standing in your way on your path to self-care. What gets in the way of doing these things in your day-to-day life?

_____

_____

_____

_____

_____

ACTIVITY ♥
My Self-Care Schedule

Now that you've identified your Self-Care roadblocks, let's be super pro-active! Let's make a schedule for the next 5 days to prioritize some self-care into your daily life. Sometimes we have to be really intentional to make big changes happen.

Self-Care Tasks: Here are some ideas, but you can do whatever works for you!

- Take a shower/bath
- Listen to music
- Watch a movie/show
- Go for a walk
- Exercise
- Ride a bike
- Play with a pet
- Stretch muscles/do yoga

- Talk to or hang with friends
- Take a rest/nap
- Go to bed on time
- Write in a journal
- Go out into nature
- Cook a healthy meal
- Read a book
- Work on a hobby

- Organize your living space
- Dance to your favorite music
- Turn off your phone 1 hour before bed
- Make your bed each day
- Drink more water
- Connect with friends
- Spend time with family

MONDAY
_____
_____
_____

TUESDAY
_____
_____
_____

WEDNESDAY
_____
_____
_____

THURSDAY
_____
_____
_____

FRIDAY
_____
_____
_____

SATURDAY
_____
_____
_____

How did it go? How did it feel? What was challenging? What did you learn?

_____
_____
_____

Check off each day you successfully prioritized self-care!

WEEKLY _____
○○○○○○○

ACTIVITY
De-Stressin' With Sketchin'

Try to Draw These Images Below!

REAL TALK:

"Keep good company, read good books, love good things and cultivate soul and body as faithfully as you can."

LOUISA MAY ALCOTT

✦ GOOD NIGHT'S SLEEP CHECKLIST ✦

YOUR NIGHTLY SELF-CARE SLEEP ROUTINE

INSPIRATION

Add things like turning off your phone an hour before bed, cozy pajamas, washing your face, brushing teeth, a face mask, putting on some nice-smelling lotion, reading a book, going to bed at the same time each night, listening to calming music.

ACTIVITY
Sleep Ritual Details

2 Hours Before Bed

Ideal Bedtime
_____PM
Ideal Asleep Time
_____PM

Self-Care Tasks I Should Do
2 Hours Before Bedtime

1 Hour Before Bed

Self-Care Tasks I Should Do
1 Hour Before Bedtime

♥

♥

♥

At Bedtime

Self-Care Tasks I Should Do
At Bedtime

Time I Went To Sleep

M [   ]

T [   ]

W [   ]

T [   ]

F [   ]

S [   ]

S [   ]

Time I Woke Up

M [   ]

T [   ]

W [   ]

T [   ]

F [   ]

S [   ]

S [   ]

How Did I Feel?

M [   ]

T [   ]

W [   ]

T [   ]

F [   ]

S [   ]

S [   ]

Noticings

After this week, what do I notice about my sleep habits and how I feel? How can I make adjustments to improve my self-care?

_____

_____

_____

_____

_____

_____

_____

_____

_____

_____

81

ACTIVITY
My Self-Care Playlist

Create a Self-Care Playlist

Create a go-to playlist for when you need it.

My Self-Care Playlist Will Feature Songs That Make Me Feel

_Happy   _Calm   _Inspired   _Safe   _Loved   _Other_____

I Will Build My Playlist On

_Spotify   _YouTube   _Apple   _Amazon   _Other_____

Name Your Playlist _____

Top 5 Songs on the List

1 _____

2 _____

3 _____

4 _____

5 _____

When Will I Use This Playlist?

_____

_____

_____

_____

_____

_____

ACTIVITY
What Makes Me Laugh?

Laughter is The Best Medicine

It's true. Laughter really is medicine. Laughter is a part of self-care because it literally reduces stress hormones like cortisol and adrenaline. Laughter boosts your immune system, gives you a physical release and it's also just a great feeling. Knowing what brings you joy and laughter is important, so let's make a list.

What and Who Makes Me Laugh and Why?

ACTIVITY
Grounding Nature Activity

What is Grounding?

Grounding is physically connecting yourself to the earth to feel a state of calm. You can do this by standing barefoot on the ground, touching the ground, touching a tree, swimming in a lake or the sea. Just connect with nature <u>physically</u>. Studies show doing this a few minutes a day can actually help you feel calmer and reduce inflammation in the body. That's powerful stuff. Give it a try this week as part of your self-care routine.

Grounding Reflection

Write about how your practice of grounding went this week. What did you feel? What did you notice?

_____

_____

_____

_____

_____

_____

_____

_____

_____

_____

_____

_____

ACTIVITY
Mood Tracker

I Woke Up Feeling

M
T
W
T
F
S
S

Mid-Day Mood Check

M
T
W
T
F
S
S

Evening Mood Check

M
T
W
T
F
S
S

Noticings

After this week, what do I notice about my moods? Can I make adjustments to improve my self-care? Are there triggers affecting my moods?

_____
_____
_____
_____
_____
_____
_____
_____
_____
_____

REAL TALK:

"Daring to set boundaries is about having the courage to love ourselves even when we risk disappointing others."

BRENÉ BROWN

86

ACTIVITY
Setting Boundaries

Learn to Say "NO!"

Saying "no" is not only OK, it's a MUST! We can't always say "yes" to everything just to please others. Doing so just makes us feel overwhelmed and often unhappy. We have to be careful not to give away too much of our time, money, energy, emotional capacity and personal space. It's a form of self-care and self-love. We need to establish boundaries and limits, so that we operate within a healthy space of self-love and self-care. Saying "no" can feel icky, but there are ways to do it maturely and respectfully. Let's think of some situations that might come up and how you might deal with them in a healthy, but assertive way.

Remember:
- "No" is a complete sentence. You don't have to explain.
- Clearly define your boundary.
- Communicate your needs.
- Be firm and assertive.

We started you off with some examples below. Below them, you can come up with four examples of situations where you need to set some healthy boundaries. Come up with the phrases you will use, so you're ready when the time comes.

A NOTE:
We know as a teenager, you're not always in a position to say "no" to your parents or teachers or other adults in authority positions. This exercise is for those times when it's OK and appropriate to set a personal boundary.

When This Happens...	How I Can Set a Boundary or Say No
Ex: Your friends keep pressuring you to join them in doing something you don't want to do.	Hey, guys. I know you're trying to include me, but this just isn't my thing. I'm going to ask that you respect that moving forward, so I don't feel pressured.
Ex: Your family member likes to argue and is pushing you on a personal belief.	We disagree on this and that's not going to change right now, so I'd like to stop discussing it. I hope you can respect that.

ACTIVITY
Setting Boundaries

Let's Set Some Boundaries!

School-Related Thing That Needs a Boundary

How I Will Set That Boundary

Family-Related Thing That Needs a Boundary

How I Will Set That Boundary

Friend-Related Thing That Needs a Boundary

How I Will Set That Boundary

Other Thing That Needs a Boundary

How I Will Set That Boundary

ACTIVITY
Mindfulness Meditation

Ahhhhh....Meditation

Meditation is the practice of focusing your mind on an object, thought or activity — like breathing, for example. This practice helps build focus and awareness, calming the overactive mind by learning to focus on one thing. There are tons of ways to do meditation, and you have to find the right method for you. Look on YouTube for 3 to 5-minute meditations to start. There are great meditation videos for teens available. Also, the Calm App has tons of free meditations. Start off with a short one.

REMEMBER
- Meditation is a practice. Your mind will wander and that's OK! Just gently bring your thoughts back to the focus. Over time, your focus will improve.
- Meditation can happen anywhere and in lots of ways. Just closing your eyes and focusing on your breathing for a few minutes is a form of meditation. It calms the mind and slows down your nervous system.

Journal:
Try a short meditation. You can just sit and breathe for a few minutes or try a meditation video on YouTube or the Calm App. Then, write down a reflection. How did it go? Did your thoughts wander? Do you feel more calm? Did it feel comfortable or uncomfortable?

_____

_____

_____

_____

_____

_____

_____

_____

_____

_____

_____

_____

ACTIVITY
Core Beliefs Shake Up

Core Beliefs

Core beliefs are the deeply held beliefs we have about ourselves and the world. Often, they can be negative.

Impact

Core beliefs shape how we think, behave, and interact with the world. But they are beliefs, not facts. We can work to change these beliefs.

People don't like me. I'm not likeable.

Core Belief

People don't want to hang out with me.

Thought

Doesn't ask friends to hang out. Keeps to herself.

Behavior

I'm not smart like the other kids in school.

Core Belief

I'm not smart enough to take hard classes or go to college.

Thought

Doesn't apply to college.

Behavior

Change is Possible!

The cool thing is that we can work on our negative core beliefs over time and shift our behaviors to be based in self-love and reality.

Let's Do It!

90

ACTIVITY
Core Beliefs Shake Up

Core Belief

Thought

Behavior

What Makes Me Believe This?

How Does This Make Me Feel?

Is This Core Belief Serving Me Well?

Journal:
Challenge yourself on this core belief. Think of reasons why this isn't based in reality. Think of facts that contradict that belief. Like, if you're calling yourself unloveable, think of three people who do, in fact, love you. Write down the ways you can challenge your core belief and begin to flip it in your mind.

_____

_____

_____

_____

_____

_____

_____

My Intended New Core Belief _____

ACTIVITY
Self-Care Tracker

Body Self-Care

M [ ]
T [ ]
W [ ]
T [ ]
F [ ]
S [ ]
S [ ]

Mind Self-Care

M [ ]
T [ ]
W [ ]
T [ ]
F [ ]
S [ ]
S [ ]

Spirit Self-Care

M [ ]
T [ ]
W [ ]
T [ ]
F [ ]
S [ ]
S [ ]

Noticings

After this week, what do I notice about how I feel? Can I make adjustments to improve my self-care? Write about how your week of self-care went!

_____
_____
_____
_____
_____
_____
_____
_____
_____

ACTIVITY
Sensory Self-Care

Your senses — sight, sound, smell, taste and touch — connect to your mind. You can care for yourself and your mind by engaging in positive and relaxing sensory experiences. For example, a good hug from someone you love feels great. That's touch. Smelling lavender feels calming. Cozying up with a soft blanket is touch! Listening to soft music can bring on serenity. Tasting a delicious flavor from childhood can bring on happy memories. Below, think about positive things you can do to give yourself some soothing, sensory self-care.

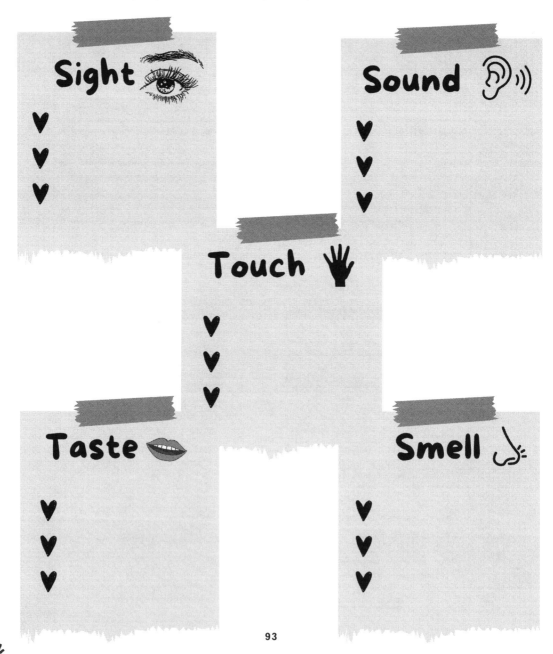

Sight

♥
♥
♥

Sound

♥
♥
♥

Touch

♥
♥
♥

Taste

♥
♥
♥

Smell

♥
♥
♥

REAL TALK:

"Knowledge is learning something every day. Wisdom is letting go of something every day."

ZEN PROVERB

94

ACTIVITY
Finding Forgiveness

Forgiveness is a form of self-care, and it's a choice. It's something you can choose to do when you are ready. Forgiveness doesn't mean you have to forget what happened. It also doesn't excuse any harm or mean that you have to keep someone in your life who hurt you. Forgiveness is for you. It's a process of letting go of the anger or hurt of a certain situation. Sometimes, we even need to forgive ourselves. Let's start the process.

Who hurt me? What emotions did this person make me feel?

_____

_____

_____

How has holding onto these negative feelings affected me?
Is this situation ongoing?

_____

_____

_____

What would you tell this person who hurt you?

_____

_____

_____

_____

Am I in a position to let these feelings go? What would it take to do that?
How will I feel when I am able to do that?

_____

_____

_____

_____

_____

ACTIVITY
What Do I Need to Let Go of?

Sometimes, we hold on tight to things that don't serve us. It's good to stop and think: What things — objects, emotions, beliefs, habits, toxic people — can I let go of to be healthier and happier? What do you think you could work on letting go of to focus on self-care, self-love and contentment? Write them in the birds! Let's start to let go!

INSPIRATION:
Here are some examples of things to let go of:

- Talking negatively about yourself
- Waiting until the last minute to do things
- Toxic friends or influences
- Old anger
- Comparing yourself to others
- Something hurtful someone said to you once

ACTIVITY
Social Media Check-In

How much time do I spend on social media per day? Do I think that's a lot, too much, just enough, too little, normal amount?

What social media apps do I spend the most time on?

Do I post on social media a lot or just look at it?

How do I feel when I look at social media? Do I compare myself to what I see on there? Do I think that my life should look like what I see? Do I think everything I see on social media is real?

_____

_____

_____

_____

_____

_____

Is social media helpful or harmful to me? Why? Explain. Are my social media habits helpful or harmful? Should I make adjustments?

_____

_____

_____

_____

_____

_____

ACTIVITY
What's the Nicest Thing You've Ever Done?

What's the nicest thing you've ever done? Describe it. Tell the story.

_____
_____
_____
_____
_____
_____
_____
_____

How did it make you feel when you did this nice thing? Explain.

_____
_____
_____
_____
_____
_____

Caring for and giving to others — altruism — actually makes us happier.
What are some ways you can build altruism into your life?

_____
_____
_____
_____

ACTIVITY
What's the Nicest Thing Ever Done For You?

What's the nicest thing someone has ever done for you?
Describe it. Tell the story.

_____
_____
_____
_____
_____
_____
_____
_____
_____

How did it make you feel when they did this nice thing? Explain.

_____
_____
_____
_____
_____
_____
_____

The good feeling you had when someone did something nice for you is something
you can pass along to others — in big and small ways. What are some SMALL
things you could do to brighten someone's day?

_____
_____
_____

LEARN
Attitude of Gratitude

Developing an Attitude of Gratitude

EMPTY
Always focusing on what's missing, what you don't have. Often feeling fearful of not getting more.

FULL
Focusing on abundance - on what you do have. Being grateful for everything you have.

IMPORTANT!

Developing an attitude of gratitude helps to shift your mindset from constantly feeling deprived to feeling satisfied and content. Being grateful doesn't mean you can't want things or feel ambition. It just means that you're operating from a place of security and self-love, rather than a place of fear and insecurity. It takes practice!

Developing an Attitude of Gratitude

WAKE UP
3 Things I Am Grateful For

Example: I am grateful for my warm house. I am grateful for the clothes I will wear today. I am grateful for the chance to learn new things at school.

DISRUPT
Interrupt Fearful Self-Talk.

Example:
My clothes are so ugly.

DISRUPT: I liked these clothes when I bought them. I can take a breath and put together something nice. I have enough. I am enough.

REPEAT
The more you repeat these things, the more your mind will believe them.

ACTIVITY
Attitude of Gratitude

Developing an Attitude of Gratitude

1 WAKE UP
3 Things I Am Grateful For

Example: I am grateful for my warm house. I am grateful for the clothes I will wear today. I am grateful for the chance to learn new things.

2 DISRUPT
Interrupt Fearful Self-Talk

Example:
My clothes are so ugly.

HOW TO DISRUPT:
I liked these clothes when I bought them. I can take a breath and put together something nice. I have enough. I am enough.

3

REPEAT
The more you repeat these things, the more your mind will believe them.

REAL TALK:

"A single act of kindness throws out roots in all directions and the roots spring up and make new trees."

AMELIA EARHART

One Week of Acts of Kindness

Holding the door. Throwing someone a smile. Picking up someone's book. Helping someone who is struggling. Offering a kind word. Acts of kindness, big and small, spread love outward <u>and</u> inward to ourselves. Often, we can get caught up in our own heads, so in doing good for others we can better see just how big and connected the world really is. Share your love. Share your good. Connect with others for good.

Record a Week of Small Acts of Kindness

M

T

W

T

F

S

S

Kindness ≳MATTERS≲

BE KIND TO YOUR MIND

Be Kind to yourself

So, how did it feel? Did it make you feel good to do good for others? Explain!

_____

_____

_____

_____

_____

SECTION 4:
SELF-GROWTH

Wow. You've done so much emotional work to get to this point. Now you're ready to look *forward*. In this section, we get to put all of the self-love and self-care you've learned about into practice and focus on your self-growth.

A growth mindset is when we are open to learning and evolving, and believe that we can take on challenging things with hard work and dedication. You can absolutely do hard things. Even when it feels tough, keep a growth mindset. You can learn from every experience and come out the other side even stronger.

This section will help you look ahead to build the life you dream of — all through a lens of self-love. You'll set goals, reflect, and let go of fears that hold you back. This is the big, life-changing stuff.

Be honest. Be true to yourself. Be open-minded and keep that growth mindset. Begin this last chapter with courage and joy because you are showing yourself. so much love by doing this exploration. Grab a pen. Settle in. Let's get started.

◻ YES! I AM READY TO START THE NEXT STEP OF MY JOURNEY OF SELF-LOVE!
DATE I STARTED THIS SECTION ____/____/____

ACTIVITY
Stepping Out of My Comfort Zone

One Thing I Could Safely Do
To Step Out of My Comfort
Zone in a BIG Way

One Thing I Could Safely Do
To Step Out of My Comfort
Zone in a SMALL Way

One Small But
Safe/Healthy Risk I
Could Try That
Would Benefit Me

What Scares Me
To Change?

What Could Change
If I Took That Risk?

My Comfort Zone

One Everyday Thing I Could
Try a Different Way That
Could Be Good for Me

One Social Thing That's Out of
My Comfort Zone, But is
Probably a Good, Healthy Move

How Could I Feel if I Was Able to Get Out of My Comfort Zone a Little Bit?

ACTIVITY
Changing Habits

Let's Change It Up!

Habits can get, well, habitual! We tend to get stuck in our habits and don't even realize that they're not healthy. Part of personal growth and self-love is recognizing the habits that aren't serving us well, and actively making a shift to healthier habits. Habits take some time to build, so don't get mad at yourself if you go a little off course. It can take anywhere from three weeks to two months of <u>consistent</u> effort to break a long-term habit. So keep going!

Unhealthy Habits

Think for a minute. What's an unhealthy habit you may have developed? Maybe it's staying up super late on your phone or eating a ton of junk food late at night. Maybe it's not doing school work until the last minute. What's your unhealthy habit?

Triggers

Now think for another minute. What are the triggers that contribute to this habit? For example, maybe you feel anxious when it's time to go to bed, so you end up scrolling on your phone. Maybe you dread doing homework, so you put it off.

Replacement Habits

Think for a minute. What steps or new habits can you make to replace this unhealthy habit? Look back at your self-care chapter for ideas. Maybe it's breaking your schoolwork down into timed chunks each day. Maybe it's setting an alarm to turn off your phone each night and creating a calm-down sleep routine.

New Habits/Steps Daily

New Habits/Steps Long-Term

ACTIVITY
Vision Board - Visualizing My Growth

WHAT TO DO: Cut out or print out images and words and tape or paste them into a collage on these 2 pages. Create a vision for your personal growth. How do you want to feel? How do you want to grow? What habits do you want to form? What beliefs do you want to prioritize?

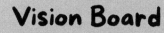

Vision Board

JOURNAL
Vision Board Reflection

Look at your completed vision board. That is your vision come to life. How does it make you feel? What does that vision feel like? Do you believe that it's possible? Part of growth is having a growth mindset — believing that you have the capacity for growth. Write about how that activity feels and where you can go with it from here.

Where's the Self-Love in Your Vision?

Look back at your vision board. Where do you see evidence of self-love and self-care? Put some examples in the hearts below.

Wow! Look at how much you've grown! Your vision for your healthy self-growth includes a lot of self-love. And if it isn't quite there yet, go back and adjust your vision a bit!

REAL TALK:

"No one can make you feel inferior without your consent."

ELEANOR ROOSEVELT

ACTIVITY
Manifesting Through Micro-Goals

Manifesting is the process of identifying your goals, believing you can achieve them, and taking actions to make them happen. We all know how to set a big goal, but small goals — or micro goals — help us set milestones that lead up to the big goal. They're mentally easier to digest as well. So let's set some goals and micro goals!

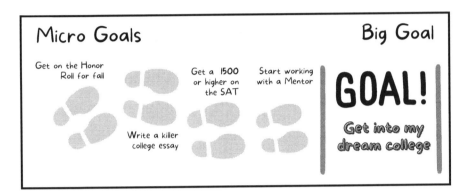

Now You Try It!

| Micro Goal 1 | Micro Goal 2 | Micro Goal 3 | Micro Goal 4 |

Big
GOAL!

| Micro Goal 1 | Micro Goal 2 | Micro Goal 3 | Micro Goal 4 |

Big
GOAL!

LEARN
S.M.A.R.T. Goals

Goals are an important step for our growth. They may change over time, but setting goals — even small ones — gives us direction and drive. S.M.A.R.T. goals are even more powerful because they go way beyond intention. They actually help you figure out HOW and WHEN you'll achieve the end result.

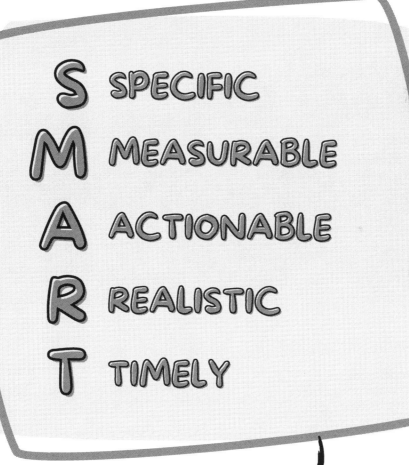

S SPECIFIC

M MEASURABLE

A ACTIONABLE

R REALISTIC

T TIMELY

<u>Specific</u>: Make your goals really detailed and specific.

<u>Measurable</u>: What does success look like for this goal?

<u>Actionable</u>: Create action steps for achieving this goal.

<u>Realistic</u>: Make sure this goal is realistic and achievable.

<u>Timely</u>: What is the timetable for this goal? How long will it take you?

S	SPECIFIC
M	MEASURABLE
A	ACTIONABLE
R	REALISTIC
T	TIMELY

GOALS!

Stuck? Don't think too hard.
This can be something simple and small.
Goals don't have to be huge or life-changing.

Social Life
S.M.A.R.T. Goals

Specific: What exactly do you want to accomplish?

Measurable: What does success look like for this goal?

Actionable: Create action steps for achieving this goal.

Realistic: Is this goal reachable? How do you know?

Timely: What is the timetable for this goal? How long will it take you?

ACTIVITY
S.M.A.R.T. Goals

S SPECIFIC
M MEASURABLE
A ACTIONABLE
R REALISTIC
T TIMELY

GOALS!

Stuck? Don't think too hard.
This can be something simple and small.
Goals don't have to be huge or life-changing.

Education/Life
S.M.A.R.T. Goals

Specific: What exactly do you want to accomplish?

Measurable: What does success look like for this goal?

Actionable: Create action steps for achieving this goal.

Realistic: Is this goal reachable? How do you know?

Timely: What is the timetable for this goal? How long will it take you?

ACTIVITY
S.M.A.R.T. Goals

S SPECIFIC
M MEASURABLE
A ACTIONABLE
R REALISTIC
T TIMELY

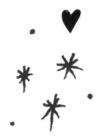

GOALS!

Stuck? Don't think too hard.
This can be something simple and small.
Goals don't have to be huge or life-changing.

Emotion/Heart
S.M.A.R.T. Goals

Specific: What exactly do you want to accomplish?

Measurable: What does success look like for this goal?

Actionable: Create action steps for achieving this goal.

Realistic: Is this goal reachable? How do you know?

Timely: What is the timetable for this goal? How long will it take you?

ACTIVITY
Prioritizing S.M.A.R.T. Goals

Which S.M.A.R.T. Goals and Steps Will I Prioritize <u>This Month?</u>

Which S.M.A.R.T. Goals and Steps Will I Prioritize in the <u>Next 3 Months?</u>

Which S.M.A.R.T. Goals and Steps Will I Prioritize in the Next 6 Months to 1 Year?

REAL TALK:

"Failure is a greater teacher than success."

CLARISSA PINKOLA ESTÉS

JOURNAL
If You Could Not Fail

Fear of failure can hold us back, but failure is a teacher. Sometimes we learn more from failure than we do from instant success. Letting go of our fear of failure empowers us to try new things — and accept that failure is temporary. We usually find a way to learn and grow and try again.

JOURNAL: <u>What would you do if you knew you could not fail?</u> What has held you back from doing this? What would happen if you failed at it? How could you learn from that failure? How you could you move on from failure if it did happen? How can you release yourself from that fear of failure and try?

Attack Your Setbacks

We all face setbacks, and they can feel really devastating! Instead of letting setbacks knock you off course, set a plan of attack. Tackle your setbacks with empowering "I will" statements that turn your setback into action. Failure and setbacks are part of the journey! Check it out.

Setback	Setback Attack
I failed the test I studied really hard for.	It was one test. I put in my best effort. <u>I will</u> reach out to my teacher and see what went wrong, so I can improve for next time.
I was kinda mean to my mom when I was tired and cranky, and I hurt her feelings.	My emotions got the best of me. Feeling bad about it shows that I care. <u>I will</u> go to my mom to sincerely apologize and offer to make her dinner.

Your Setback	Setback Attack

ACTIVITY
Places I Want To Go!

The List of Places I Want To Go!

Make a list of allllllll the places you'd like to go. Don't worry about money or limits or failure. Just make the list. It will help you see what's important in your heart and the places you most want to see in life.

ACTIVITY
Things I Want to Do & Try

The List of Things I Want To Do & Try!

Make a list of alllllllll the things you'd like to do and try. Don't worry about money or limits or failure. Just make the list. It will help you see what's important in your heart and the things you most want to achieve.

123

JOURNAL
How Will I Feel When...

Look back through all of these goal-setting pages. Look at all of the awesome goals you've set. Hello, amazing. Take a few minutes and visualize your life _accomplishing_ these goals. Imagine yourself as the girl who lives these dreams. How will you feel when you've reached these goals? How will you be different? How will life feel? Write about it! Visualize it and share it in detail below.

_____
_____
_____
_____
_____
_____
_____
_____
_____
_____
_____
_____
_____
_____
_____
_____
_____
_____
_____
_____
_____
_____
_____
_____

Here's the thing. Your goals and aspirations are not imaginary. They _can_ be real. Sure, you may not always get every single thing you want exactly as you want it, but you can work to create the life you dream of. Make the life you want happen by speaking it out loud. Give power to your goals by setting manageable micro-goals and tracking your progress. Use the voice inside your mind for good. Stop negative self-talk in its tracks and start _encouraging_ yourself. Take time to visualize your goals as reality, and think how good it will feel to live the life you've imagined. Then, start working toward it.

ACTIVITY
Dear Past Me

Write a Letter to Your Past Self

What would you tell your past self? What message would you send her?
Write a letter to the girl you once were from the girl you are today.

ACTIVITY
Dear Future Me

Write a Letter to Your Future Self

What would you tell your future self? What message would you send her?
Write a letter to the woman you will become.

REAL TALK:

"Always be a first-rate version of yourself instead of a second-rate version of somebody else."

JUDY GARLAND

ACTIVITY
My 8 Words to Live By

Own your POWER

My 8 Words to Live By

Come up with 8 powerful words to live by. Write them in the bubbles below. These words should represent what you believe, what you hold most dear, and what empowers you.

INSPIRATIONAL EXAMPLES:

Courage
Honesty
Bravery
Kindness
Empowerment
Confidence
Love

STEP 2:
Then, choose 1 word from your list that feels the most important.

_____

What does this mean to you?

_____

_____

_____

_____

_____

_____

_____

_____

What Do You Wish Others Knew?

i am One of a Kind

What do you wish others knew about you? Write it all down here.
What are the things that people don't quite get or know about you
— but you wish they did?

_____

_____

_____

_____

_____

_____

_____

_____

_____

_____

_____

_____

_____

_____

_____

_____

_____

_____

_____

_____

How would it feel if other people knew this stuff about you?
Could you tell them? Why or why not?

_____

_____

_____

_____

ACTIVITY
Overcoming Self-Doubt

A Time I Experienced Major Self-Doubt

What Did I Do to Get Past It?

How Can I Apply Those Actions in the Future The Next Time I Feel Self-Doubt?

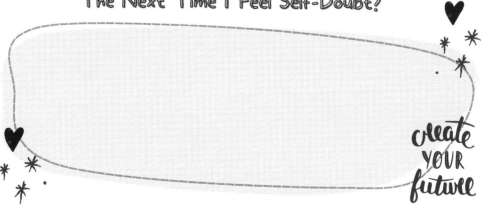

ACTIVITY
Rock My Confidence

What Gives Me Confidence? Why?

What Shakes My Confidence? Why?

How can I work with this or around this?

ACTIVITY
Letting Go of Fears

What Are Some Fears You'd Like to Let Go of?

We all have fears. Some are easy to pinpoint — like being afraid of spiders — and others are a little more difficult to figure out. Sometimes we don't even know we're holding ourselves back out of fear. Check out the list below of common emotional fears. See if any of them spark anything in you. Or, think about some of your own emotional fears that might be standing in your way. Make a list below of the fears you'd like to work on letting go of!

COMMON EMOTIONAL FEARS

Change
Failure
Hurt
Judgement
Rejection
Lack of control
Missing out
Uncertainty
Not being good enough
Making the wrong choice
Responsibility
Saying the wrong thing
Imposter syndrome (feeling like a fake)
Fear of challenge
The unknown
Loss
Abandonment

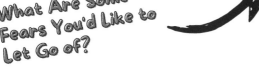

1 What is the #1 fear holding you back?

_____

What would happen if you were free from your number 1 emotional fear from the previous page? What would life look like if that fear were gone? How would you be different? What would you do differently? Describe that life in detail. Imagine it as if it were true.

_____
_____
_____
_____
_____
_____
_____
_____
_____
_____
_____
_____
_____
_____
_____
_____
_____
_____
_____

Now that you imagined that life, how did it feel? Do you believe that it's possible to get to that place? Why or why not? What would need to happen?

_____
_____
_____

LEARN
Letting Go of Fear

ALL IN YOUR HANDS

There are real things you can do to start letting go of emotional fears that hold you back. It's not instant. It's not always easy, but with awareness and practice, you can begin to release some long-held beliefs and fears that stand in the way of living your best life.

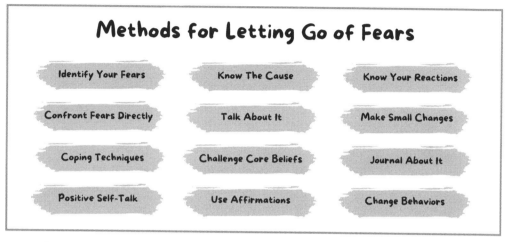

Methods for Letting Go of Fears

Identify Your Fears | Know The Cause | Know Your Reactions
Confront Fears Directly | Talk About It | Make Small Changes
Coping Techniques | Challenge Core Beliefs | Journal About It
Positive Self-Talk | Use Affirmations | Change Behaviors

EXAMPLE:
FEAR: I am afraid of being judged, so I never speak up in class.

WHAT THE METHODS LOOK LIKE
- <u>Identify the Fear:</u> A fear of judgment and rejection.
- <u>Know the Cause:</u> In 3rd grade, a boy made fun of my answer in class and now I'm afraid to speak up in school.
- <u>Know Your Reactions:</u> I shy away from being called on. I never volunteer.
- <u>Confront It Directly:</u> One option is to just boldly do the thing I'm most afraid of and raise my hand even though I'm scared.
- <u>Talk About It:</u> I can speak to my teacher about it and see if she can support me.
- <u>Make Small Changes:</u> I can try to speak up during small group work.
- <u>Coping Techniques:</u> Take a slow deep breath before speaking. Pick a focal point.
- <u>Challenge Core Beliefs:</u> My fear of judgment has made me believe that I am not smart enough to share my answers in class. That is not true. It's OK to be wrong sometimes. My voice matters, and I should share it.
- <u>Journal About It:</u> I will write about this every day this week in my journal.
- <u>Positive Self-Talk:</u> My voice matter and deserves to be shared.
- <u>Use Affirmations:</u> I am smart and capable. My voice matters.
- <u>Change Behaviors:</u> I will try to raise. my hand at least once a day.

ACTIVITY
Letting Go of Fear

ALL
IN
YOUR
HANDS

Identify Your Fears	Know The Cause	Know Your Reactions
Confront Fears Directly	Talk About It	Make Small Changes
Coping Techniques	Challenge Core Beliefs	Journal About It
Positive Self-Talk	Use Affirmations	Change Behaviors

Identify your emotional fear.

Where do you think this fear comes from?

How do you react to this fear?

How does this fear impact your life?

Look at the options at the top of this page and the examples on the previous page. What methods could you use to try to let go or reduce this fear in your life?

What would that method look like in practice? Describe it below. See previous page for examples.

ACTIVITY
Negative Thought Blaster

Negative thoughts are often based on a distorted or twisted view of reality. The good news? You can change negative thought patterns with practice. It might feel wonky at first, but with time, disrupting negative thoughts will help improve your negative thinking.

Negative Thought Blaster

Negative Thought	Distortion Filter	Makes Me Feel	Disrupt The Thought
 I'll never be pretty like her.	**Negative Focus** Ignoring the positive and only focusing on negative.	Sad, Unworthy	Pretty comes in many forms. Comparing myself to others isn't useful. Accepting and loving myself is a better use of my time and thoughts.
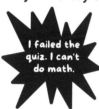 I failed the quiz. I can't do math.	**Overgeneralizing** When one bad thing happens, and you think it's a pattern.	Dumb, Incapable	It was one quiz. Math can be challenging, but I can do hard things. If I need support, I can look for it. I am capable of mastering challenging topics.

Now You Try!

Negative Thought	Distortion Filter	Makes Me Feel	Disrupt The Thought
	How Is This Thought Distorting/ Twisting the Truth? ––––––––––– ––––––––––– –––––––––––	How does this thought make me feel? ––––––––––– ––––––––––– ––––––––––– –––––––––––	Change the thought into a positive, realistic statement. ––––––––––– ––––––––––– ––––––––––– –––––––––––

"You're going to be great. Spend less time tearing yourself apart, worrying if you're good enough. You are good enough."

REESE WITHERSPOON

ACTIVITY
I Am Worthy of Love

You are worthy

I Am Worthy of Love Because...

138

What Does Happiness Mean To You?

Happiness looks different for everyone. It's a state of mind, not a destination. Being happy doesn't mean that our lives are totally without challenge or pain. Happiness is a general sense of satisfaction and purpose. Think about what happiness means to you. Journal about it. When did you feel happy? What do you think would make you happy in life? Describe happiness for you.

_____

_____

_____

_____

_____

_____

_____

_____

_____

_____

_____

_____

_____

_____

_____

_____

_____

_____

_____

How do your goals align with your vision of happiness? Do they work together?

_____

_____

_____

_____

_____

ACTIVITY
Rejection Rescue

Rejection Rescue

Everyone experiences rejection at different points in their life — and it definitely doesn't feel good. But living in fear of rejection can stop you from taking action. That's worse. Rejection stings a bit, but it's temporary. It's the unfortunate price we pay for putting ourselves out there and taking healthy emotional risks. Relationships end, you might not get the part in the play, you might get cut from the team, or you might not get invited to the party — but don't shrink away from life because rejection is a possibility. Rejection is a passing feeling, and by staying mindful of the feelings and beliefs it creates, you can make sure it's always a short-term feeling.

Think of a time you experienced feelings of rejection. What happened?

_____

How did it feel? Describe it.

_____

_____

What self-beliefs did this rejection lead to? Example: Not getting into the school play could make you believe that you're not good enough.

_____

_____

Go back to the Core Beliefs exercise on page 90. Think about how those core beliefs lead to behaviors. Example: Not getting into the play leads to believing you're not good enough, which leads to never auditioning again. Now, challenge the self-beliefs that came up from your rejection. How can you change this thinking?

_____

_____

_____

_____

How can you make this rejection a temporary hurt instead of carrying it around with you through long-term beliefs and behaviors?

_____

_____

Write a Self-Love Letter to Yourself

You've done a lot of emotional exploration in this book. Write a beautiful letter to yourself today, focusing on self-love. Write a note to the girl you are today. She is strong, lovable, smart and full of potential. Be kind. Show yourself a little love. Save this note for when you're older.

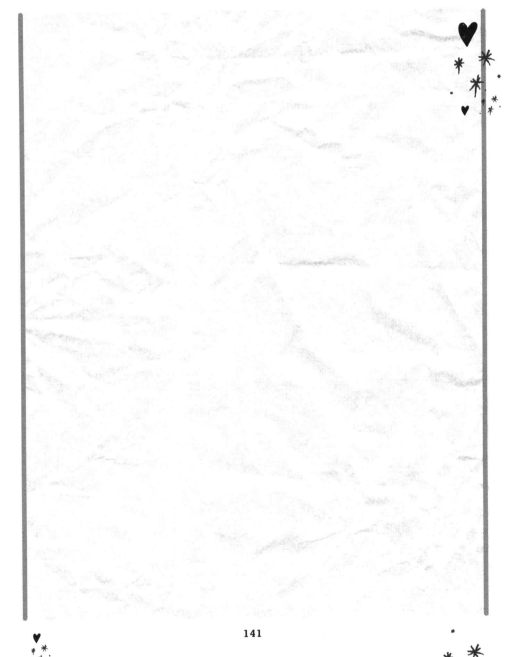

You Did It!

YOU'RE AWESOME

You finished this journal! What an amazing accomplishment. Look back through all of the emotional work you did in this book. See how much you shared and how much you've grown. This is only the beginning of your journey. Keep these lessons in your heart and mind, and keep practicing these ideas. We are always evolving.

You are worthy of self-love.
You are worthy of self-care.
Self-love allows us to love others fully and joyfully.
Self-love allows us to fully live the life we deserve.

Last thoughts... How does it feel to have completed this journey? How do you think you've grown? What's your next step?

_____

_____

_____

_____

_____

_____

_____

Extra Writing Space

Extra Writing Space

Extra Writing Space

Extra Writing Space

Extra Writing Space

Extra Writing Space

Extra Writing Space

Extra Writing Space

Extra Writing Space

SELF-LOVE JOURNAL FOR TEEN GIRLS

LOVE yourself

Made in the USA
Middletown, DE
05 October 2023